This Journal belongs to

_____

WITH OUR **THOUGHTS** *we make the* WORLD.

Siddhartha Gautama

It could be that there's **only one word** and it's all we need. It's here **in this pencil.** Every pencil in the world is like this. **W.S. Merwin**

CRAZY just might WORK.

Nothing is original.

Steal from anywhere that resonates with inspiration or fuels your imagination. Devour old films, new films, music, books, paintings, photographs, poems, dreams, random conversations, architecture, bridges, street signs, trees, clouds, bodies of water, light and shadows. Select only things to steal from that speak directly to your soul. If you do this, your work (and theft) will be authentic. Authenticity is invaluable; originality is non-existent. And don't bother concealing your thievery—celebrate it if you feel like it. In any case, always remember what Jean-Luc Godard said: "It's not where you take things from—it's where you take them to." Jim Jarmusch

What is now PROVED was once only imagined.

William Blake

It shall be done, **sometime,** somewhere.

Ophelia Guyon Browning

Visualize this thing
YOU WANT.
See it, feel it, believe in it.
MAKE
YOUR
MENTAL
— blueprint —
AND BEGIN.
Robert Collier

Things are only **impossible** until they're not.

Jean-Luc Picard

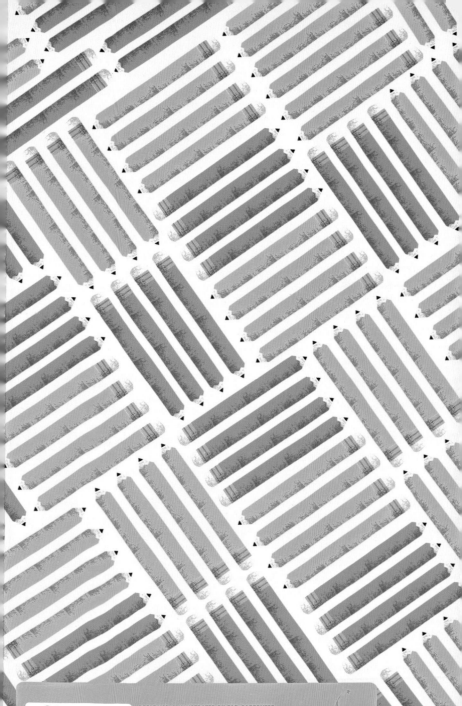

DESIGNED & ILLUSTRATED BY TAD CARPENTER.

What you do makes a difference. Enjoy the world gently.
Printed with soy inks on chlorine-free paper.

© COMPENDIUM INC. ALL RIGHTS RESERVED.
3RD PRINTING. PRINTED IN CHINA. LIVE-INSPIRED.COM

COMPENDIUM
INCORPORATED

live inspired.

QUILL & PRESS
STATIONERS

ISBN 978-1-935414-18-6

9 781935 414186